Endpapers One of the
Federal German Navy's
Westland Lynx HAS 2s
operating from a Bremen
class frigate.

Opposite A Federal German
Army operated Bell UH-1D.

This book was devised and produced by
Multimedia Publications (UK) Ltd

Editor: Jeff Groman
Design: John Strange and Associates
Picture Research: Military Archive &
Research Services – John & Diane Moore.
Production: Arnon Orbach

ISBN 0 8317 4200 3

First published in the United States of
America by Gallery Books, an imprint of
W. H. Smith Publishers Inc., 112 Madison
Avenue, New York, NY 10016

Originated by D. S. Colour International Ltd,
London.
Printed by Cayfosa, Barcelona, Spain
Dep. Leg. B - 35510 - 1984

MILITARY HELICOPTERS

Hugh W. Cowin

GALLERY BOOKS
An Imprint of W. H. Smith Publishers Inc.
112 Madison Avenue
New York City 10016

CONTENTS

Introduction

While the emergence of the military helicopter as a vital element in both the conduct of a battle and the equally important task of battle support and resupply has only been brought about within the relatively recent past, the helicopter, as a concept at least, has been with us for over 500 years.

The first recorded helicopter concept to be put on paper flowed from the visionary pen of the multi-talented Italian, Leonardo Da Vinci, who, in 1483, drew up a scheme for a manpowered "Aerial Screw Machine". Others, largely unknown but including Britain's Sir George Cayley in 1843, were to take up the challenge of producing a flying machine supported by rotating wings through most of the next four centuries: all to little avail.

The first helicopters
Once the fundamental problem of producing relatively lightweight, high power-to-weight engines had been licked around the start of this century, the helicopter, as such, became credible. Indeed, between the Breguet-Richet 4-rotor machine flown in September 1907 and the Spaniard Isacco's single powered rotor design of 1929, no less than eight differing designs are known to have flown with varying degrees of success. By June 1936, the known tally of relatively successful helicopter designs had risen to twelve, of which the latest, the Focke Achgelis Fa-61, was to take the world by storm.

Left A line-astern formation of British Army Westland Lynx AH1s.

Below Sea King Wessex 1 and Gazelle helicopters.

Generally considered to be the world's first truly practical helicopter, the twin-rotored Fa-61 rapidly smashed all preceding helicopter records for speed, height and endurance by lavish margins with figures such as 76 mph, 8,000 feet and 1.33 hours. By 1941, both the German Navy and the US Army were placing orders for the world's first two production helicopters in the shapes of the Flettner Fl-282 Kolibri and Sikorsky R-4, respectively. The modern helicopter had emerged.

CHAPTER 1
Enter the Helicopter

As with virtually every other sector of aviation development during the latter part of the 1930s, it was the Germans who were to play a major part in the shaping of the latterday helicopter, not only in a technical sense, but also in the molding of its mainstream roles.

As early as 1938, Lufthansa, the German airline, impressed by the already proven performance of the Fa-61, undertook to fund the development of a scaled-up version that was to become the Fa-223 Drache. This, with its ability to lift a sling load of 2,000 lbs or four fully equipped troopers, could well lay claim to being the world's first production transport helicopter. In parallel with the Focke Achgelis work, another German, Anton Flettner, was busily developing a more compact family of helicopters leading to the ship-going Fl-282 Kolibri, built specifically to undertake anti-submarine duties. However, pressure for higher production of fixed wing aircraft along with the subsequent impact of Allied bombing attacks took their toll on the overall pace of German helicopter development. As a result, only handfuls of machines ever actually entered operational service.

US developments
In America during the late 1930s the expatriat Russian, Igor Sikorsky, who had built his first helicopter in 1910, resurrected his interest in rotary-winged flight. In September 1939, Sikorsky began tethered flight trials with his VS-300 single rotor machine, followed by free flight testing of the aircraft in May 1940. Impressed by Sikorsky's efforts in this field, the US Army, seeing the helicopter's value both as a rescue and communication vehicle, ordered his VS-316 design straight from the drawing board in late 1941. This helicopter, by now given the Army designation XR-4, flew for the first time in January 1942.

In all, 114 R-4s were to be built, many of which were transferred to the US Navy, Royal Air Force and Royal

A Royal Navy operated Sikorsky R-4.

Navy for their evaluation. By August 1943, Sikorsky was flying his much more powerful S-51/R-5 design, the first of the truly mass-produced Sikorsky helicopters, built not only in the US but also by Westland in Britain, who produced a total of 183 license-built S-51s mainly for Royal Air Force or Royal Navy use.

In 1942, another American, Lawrence Bell, turned his attention to the helicopter, commencing tethered flight testing of his Model 30 in the following year. Bell's painstaking work was to prove as fruitful as that of Sikorsky's, leading to the renowned Model 47 design, first flown in December 1945. Under the US Army Air Force designation of H-13, the Bell Model 47 remains in worldwide military and civil use today.

In Britain and France little of any significance was to be done in terms

Above The Focke Achgelis Fa-61 of 1936. While by no means the first helicopter to fly, the Fa-61's performance and reliability totally eclipsed all earlier machines.
Below Igor Sikorsky piloting his VS-300 during early tests in 1940.
Lower Right A US Army Bell H-13E on casualty evacuation duties in Korea. This machine plays a starring role at the beginning of every episode of the long-running television series M.A.S.H.
Top Right Bell's Arthur Young carrying out tethered testing of a working model helicopter. This work, started in 1941, led to the legendary Bell Model 47/H-13.

of home-grown helicopter development until well into the latter half of the 1940s in the case of the British, or early 1950s where France was concerned.

Post-war development
The year 1947 was to prove the first major milestone in the development of Britain's home-based helicopter development, seeing the first flights of the relatively conventional Bristol Sycamore and the less conventional Fairey Gyrodyne. The Sycamore, followed by the much larger, tandem-rotored Bristol Belvedere transport helicopter, first flown in January 1952, was to be the first British-developed helicopter to enter into widespread British service use. The Fairey Gyrodyne evolved by stages into the record-setting, 40-passenger Fairey Rotodyne in which the Royal Air Force was showing an intense interest even before its first flight in November 1957. This military interest remained up until the time that the Rotodyne development was shelved in 1962, largely due to ongoing governmental policy shifts, rather than for any technical reason. In 1958, all home-based British helicopter development being undertaken by Bristol, Fairey and Saunders-Roe was placed in the hands of Westland Helicopter by government dictate.

French efforts to develop a helicopter industry were initiated in

the early 1950s, leading to the Sud-Ouest SO 1220 Djinn light observation type, first flown in January 1953. The Djinn was followed just over two years later, in March 1955, by the first flight of the larger Sud-Ouest SO 3130 Alouette light utility type, of which well over 1,300 examples were eventually to be built.

The only other country involved in helicopter development during the latter 1940s and early 1950s was Soviet Russia, whose Yakolev Yak-24 'Horse', a large, tandem-rotored transport machine, made its first flight in July 1953.

Above One of the 130 British Army operated Bell Model 47s, all of which were license-built by either Agusta or Westland.

Above A float-equipped Piasecki (now Boeing Vertol) H-21A Workhorse employed in the search and rescue role by the US Air Force.

Left A Piasecki H-21C of the French Air Force, who made extensive use of the type both in Indo-China and Algeria.

Above A US Air Force Sikorsky H-5D, specifically used on search and rescue duties.

Right A Sikorsky H-19A of the US Air Force. Variants of this 12-seat utility helicopter were used by all three US air arms, plus many overseas armed services.

9

Above Britain's first home-
developed production
helicopter, the Bristol
Sycamore, was operated by
both the Royal Air Force and
British Army as well as by
Belgium, Federal Germany
and Australia. In all, 178
Sycamores were built.

Right A Piasecki (now
Boeing Vertol) H-25
Retriever of the US Air
Force. Several hundred of
this type were built for the
US Navy/Marines, Army
and Air Force, along with
the services of Canada and
France.

CHAPTER 2
Vertical Infantry

As with virtually any other aspect of military development, the helicopter's evolution flourished particularly during the 1950s and 1960s, largely due to the impetus provided by a series of ongoing wars, ranging from Korea and Malaysia at the start of the period, through Indo-China and Algeria, to the Middle East and Vietnam in later years.

As either US troops or US-built helicopters were to take part in virtually all of these campaigns, with the sole exception of the British action in Malaysia, it should come as little surprise that it was the American military helicopter and its supporting industry that was to reap the major benefits. Equally clearly, the US Army, as purchaser, operator and future requirement specifier, played a crucial role in the overall scheme of things.

The needs of the US Army
For the latter part of the 1940s, the US Army, who had had its air force element decoupled from it in 1947, were largely content to allow the newly formed US Air Force to lead in terms of helicopter development; a state of affairs that was to persist into the early 1950s. In hindsight, it is clear that, from the Army's viewpoint, this was a rather unsatisfactory period

during which, largely by Air Force default, the US Navy were allowed more and more to dictate the kind of helicopters being drawn up by Sikorsky, Bell and Piasecki (now Boeing Vertol). Realising this, the US Army started to push their own requirements, commencing in 1955, when they issued the specification that gave birth to the 12-troop carrying Bell Model 204/205/212 family, perhaps better known as the UH-1 series.

Below Although never put into production, the sole US Air Force funded Hughes XH-17 pointed the way towards the truly massive flying crane loadlifter.

Bottom While far less ambitious than the Hughes XH-17, Sikorsky's S-56 could still lift sizable loads, including internally-carried light vehicles. Operated by the US Marines as the HR2S and by the US Army as the CH-37A Mojave, a total of 154 were built.

Below and Bottom The tandem-rotored Bristol Belvedere HC1, the Royal Air Force's first sizable transport helicopter. Able to carry either 30 troops or an underslung load of up to 6,000 lbs, 26 production examples were delivered during the early 1960s.

In 1959, the Army ordered its first large assault type in the shape of the Boeing Vertol CH-47 Chinook, completing a four-card trick with its 1962 specifications for a light scouting helicopter and an armed and armored gunship; needs that led directly to the Hughes OH-6 Cayuse and Bell AH-1 Hueycobra respectively. Thus, by the mid-1960s, as the US were becoming more and more involved in South East Asia, their Army was in a position to provide all of the various mission types required to transport, land and support their fighting troops along the tactical lines that they had already devised during the early 1960s.

Only one other country has been able, and then only in part, to match the development of the US battlefield helicopter, namely Soviet Russia. The Soviets have tended to concentrate their efforts around the development of even larger sized assault and transport helicopters, plus formidable gunships in the shape of the Mil-24 'Hind'. In general, the pace of Soviet military helicopter development has lagged somewhat behind that of the US – the Soviets have yet to produce a machine comparable to the Bell UH-1.

Today, with their large number of rebuilt CH-47 Chinooks, backed by the smaller Sikorsky UH-60A Black Hawk and Hughes AH-64 Apache gunships coming into service, the US Army looks set to maintain its dominant influence on the battlefield helicopter and its use.

Upper Right A US Army Boeing Vertol CH-47D Chinook demonstrating its battlefield usefulness by airlifting in a heavy field howitzer.

Lower Left A Chinook HC1 of the Royal Air Force lifting a Scorpion light tank.

Upper Left This US Army CH-47D Chinook is one of more than 900 so far delivered to numerous services worldwide since 1962.

Lower Right The US Army made much use of the 12 troop-carrying Bell UH-1D in Vietnam, often operated, as here, in sufficiently large numbers to airlift more than a thousand infantry rapidly in or out of the battle area.

Below The US Marine Corps made large-scale use of the Bell UH-1 in their South East Asian operations, this pair being UH-1Es.

Right Prior to the 1979 Iranian Revolution, Iran placed a series of large orders for the Bell Model 214, a development of the UH-1, of which 335 had been handed over when deliveries were halted.

Left The role versatility of the military helicopter is demonstrated by this US Army UH-1D equipped with outrigger mine dispensers, each capable of laying a track of up to 70 anti-tank or anti-personnel mini-mines.

Below and Opposite The French-developed Aerospatiale SA 330 H/L Puma medium-sized transport helicopter has been a valuable export earner with sales to around 25 overseas countries, plus the 48 SA 330C models built for the Royal Air Force. Including French-operated Pumas, more than 600 have been sold, of which the vast majority are for military use.

Above The US Air Force's Sikorsky HH-60D Night Hawk is a specialized, all-weather search and rescue variant of the US Army's UH-60A Black Hawk.

Right and Opposite The Sikorsky UH-60A Black Hawk has now largely replaced the Bell UH-1 as the US Army's prime squad-sized troop transport. UH-60As first saw action in Grenada during early 1984.

Above The Hughes Model 500 MD Defender, a development of the company's OH-6, has sold to a number of nations, including Israel. This machine carries four TOIV anti-tank missiles.

Right A HOT anti-tank missile equipped MBB Bo-105 of the Federal German Army, who operate more than 200 Bo-105s.

Left A Danish-operated Hughes OH-6A employed on scouting and communications duties. Over 1,550 were built, mainly for the US Army.

Below One of 30 Dutch Army operated MBB Bo-105s. More than 220 military models have been exported to or license-built in countries as far afield as Spain and Indonesia.

Left Still in service with the British Army after more than 21 years is Westland's turbo shaft-powered and highly respected Scout AH1.

Below A Westland Commando of the Egyptian Air Force. The Commando is an Anglicized development of Sikorsky's S.61/SH-3 Sea King.

←DANGER

G·BDGW

CHAPTER 3
The Helicopter Goes to Sea

1985 marks the 21st anniversary of the Royal Navy's initial operational deployment of the anti-submarine torpedo carrying Westland Wasp from the decks of its Tribal class frigates. This event, along with the only slightly later Royal Canadian Navy deployment of the much larger and more capable Sikorsky SH-3 Sea King, was to usher in the era of the modern, small ship-going anti-submarine helicopter, now very much taken for granted by navies large and small throughout the world.

Much of the early post-World War II naval helicopter development effort was led by the US Navy, who in conjunction with Sikorsky and Bell and later largely solely with Sikorsky had evolved an ever-more effective series of anti-submarine types in the shape of the 1953 Bell HSL-1, the 1954 Sikorsky S-58/HSS and 1959 Sikorsky S-61/SH-3 Sea King. The one drawback to these US Navy developments centered on the fact that all of these aircraft were unable to operate on anything smaller than either an aircraft carrier or large, clear-decked transport ship.

As to the British and Canadian development work on the small ship-going helicopter, it is interesting to note the quite fundamentally different approaches chosen by the two services. In the case of the British, the Wasp represented about the smallest machine capable of lifting two men and two lightweight torpedoes. In terms of its impact on the parent ship, the Wasp made minimal demands, necessitating only the addition of a light hangar, topped by a fold-down landing platform or helipad. In contrast, to operate the Sea King, the Canadians had to virtually redesign their frigate fleet to have around fifty per cent of their upper deck area given over to the hangarage and helipad needed to accommodate a single Sea King.

Saving space
With the exception of the Japanese Navy, who have elected to follow the Canadian pattern, most of the world's navies have adopted the British approach of attempting to minimize the amount of ship weight and space devoted to helicopter operations and stowage. Nowhere is such a desire more apparent than in the case of the Italian-developed Esmeraldas class corvette of only 700 tons full displacement, which, while lacking a hangar, has an elevated helipad large enough to operate an Agusta-Bell AB 212ASW helicopter.

Today, there are approximately 1,200 small ship-going naval helicopters, ranging from the high capability/high cost Sikorsky SH-60B Seahawk and Westland Lynx, through

Left The US Navy's Sikorsky HSS-1/SH-34 Seabat, put into service in 1955, is generally considered to be the first effective sub-killer, particularly following its re-engining to turbine power carried out by the British, who license-built the type as the Westland Wessex. *Below* The Sikorsky SH-60B Seahawk, seen here in prototype form, represents the current generation of US Navy sub-killers.

the French-developed Aerospatiale AS 365 Dauphin II to the less expensive, if somewhat more operationally limited, Hughes Model 500D ASW and MBB Bo-105. Of these aircraft, nearly 150 now carry a useful secondary anti-ship strike capability, thanks to recent development in compacting the size of both the missile and its associated electronics.

Below Sikorsky's SH-3 Sea King, developed specifically for the US Navy, represented a major breakthrough in anti-submarine helicopter capability and will remain in widespread service into the next century, some forty years after its operational debut.

Right An Agusta license-built SH-3D Sea King of the Italian Navy. While Sikorsky no longer produce the type it remains in production in both Britain and Italy.

Above A Royal Navy Westland-Sikorsky Sea King HAS 5. Westland have been particularly successful in selling the machine to overseas users.

Right A Westland-Sikorsky Sea King HAS 2 hastily fitted with a long range search radar for deployment with Britain's Falklands garrison forces.

Below A US Navy 31 Helicopter Squadron Kaman SH-2F Seasprite coming in to land aboard the aft helicopter platform of a Knox class frigate. The Seasprite still provides the bulk of the US Navy small ship sub-killing capability.

Right This US Navy Kaman NHH-2D is seen carrying out early shipboard-going trials aboard the Belknap class cruiser USS Fox (CG 38).

Upper Left The Sikorsky MH-53E Super Stallion will shortly enter the US Navy as an aerial minesweeper, supplementing and ultimately replacing the fleet of earlier MH-53D machines currently employed on these duties.

Lower Left Sikorsky's SH-60B Seahawk shipboard sub-killer, recently introduced into US Navy service, is a derivative of the UH-60A Black Hawk.

Near Left Sikorsky's CH-53E Super Stallion provides the US Marine Corps with a massive airborne heavy assault capability, with more than 140 planned for delivery to the service by 1992, plus models for the US Navy.

Center A US Navy SH-60B Seahawk operating over San Diego. Original plans called for the purchase of 204 Seahawks, but this number may be increased.

Below Two US Marine Corps' CH-53E Super Stallions refuel in flight from a US Navy Lockheed KC-130H Hercules tanker.

Below The US Navy still operates a large number of Bel UH-1Ns on inter-ship utility and communications duties.

Left The Soviet Navy's Kamov Ka-25 'Hormone' still provides the bulk of Russia's ship-going anti-submarine and anti-ship targeting capability.

Below A French Navy Aerospatiale SA321G Super Frelon, seen here armed with the ship-killing Exocet missile.

Upper Left The joint Anglo-Italian European Helicopter Industries EH-101, seen here in Italian Navy colors, is scheduled to enter service during the 1980s as a Sea King replacement with both countries.

Lower Left The Mil-4 'Hound' was the Soviet Navy's first sub-killer, but was always operated from land bases. A few remain in service with a number of Eastern Bloc navies, including that of mainland China.

Upper Right The US Marine Corps employs the Bell AH-1T gunship in support of amphibious troop landings from US Navy assault ships, such as their Tarawa class vessels.

Below One of the early US Marine Corps' Bell AH-1Js showing its ability to operate from a US Navy frigate's helipad.

Right The Hughes Model 500MD ASW represents about the most compact sub-killing helicopter available. A number of these small ship-going machines have been sold to Far Eastern navies.

Below An Italian Navy Agusta-Bell AB212ASW sub-killer. Developed in Italy from the Bell UH-1N, more than 100 AB212ASWs have been sold to a number of navies around the world.

Below All US Navy
helicopter pilots have to
start somewhere and,
currently, it is the Bell
TH-57A that provides their
basic training.

Above A Royal Navy Westland Lynx HAS2 equipped with four Sea Skua anti-ship missiles; a combination that proved highly effective during the 1982 Falkland Islands campaign.

Below A Westland Lynx HAS2 going aboard the Royal Navy Leander class frigate HMS *Danae* (F47). Around 200 naval Lynx have been sold.

Upper Right This French Navy-operated Lynx HAS2, here seen aboard the destroyer *Georges Leygues* (D640), is one of 40 delivered. The Georges Leygues class ships each carry two Lynx.

Lower Right Simply keeping a shipboard helicopter aboard can present problems as can be seen with this Lynx HAS2 aboard the Royal Navy destroyer HMS *Birmingham* (D86).

Above The Aerospatiale SA319B Alouette III is operated with a number of navies, including that of France, shown here, who retain the type for anti-submarine helicopter crew training.

Left Crew members of a Mexican Navy Uribe class patrol vessel manhandle the ship's MBB Bo-105 ASW into the maindeck hangar.

Upper Right Although primarily operated as a Royal Navy training type, these Westland-built Aerospatiale SA341 Gazelle HT2s can double as light communications helicopters, several serving in this role from Royal Navy ships taking part in the Falkand Islands conflict.

Lower Right Still in widespread naval service today, the Westland Wasp became the world's first small ship-going sub-killer when it was first deployed aboard Royal Navy Tribal class frigates in 1965.

CHAPTER 4
The Tank Killers

Unquestionably, it was the US Army during the early 1960s that led the world into the development of the armed and armored gunship helicopter with the Bell AH-1 HueyCobra. As originally designed, the AH-1 was a single engined machine but, thanks to subsequent US Marine Corps support, emerged as a twin-engined machine in later models, providing a higher degree of crew safety from battle damage. Over the years, the AH-1 family has grown not only in terms of total installed power, but also in the range and weight of weaponry that can be hung from it, including cannon, rockets and ever more potent anti-tank missiles. Today's US Army's Hughes AH-64 Apache, with its ability to carry up to eight long range Hellfire anti-tank missiles, plus 1,200 rounds of 30 mm ammunition, benefits from the massive bank of US Army gunship operating experience: an input that has helped forge its unprecedented ability to both hand out and tolerate more combat punishment than any previous helicopter.

Escalating costs
Needless to say, the cost of developing such machines as the AH-64 is considerable, running at around 12.6 million dollars each in 1984 values when all research costs are recovered over the currently authorised 515 aircraft programme. On this basis, it is fairly self evident that few services outside those of the world's leading nations could afford such a machine. However, advances in the fields of anti-tank missiles and electronics in recent years have brought the tank-killing helicopter within the reach of the less affluent armies around the world. Due to the development of 'off-the-shelf' weaponry and the associated aiming equipment, it is now quite possible to buy a virtually standard commercial

Right France's Aerospatiale SA341L, seen here cannon equipped, not only serves with the French Army, but has exported in large numbers to many overseas military air arms.

Above Despite the advent of the AH-64A Apache, the US Army's Bell AH-1S HueyCobra will remain in front-line service for many years yet, thanks to a major programme of airframe relifing and equipment modernization.

Below Iran operates the Bell AH-1J HueyCobra, 202 being delivered prior to the 1979 Iranian Revolution. Around 60 can carry four TOW anti-tank missiles.

Upper Right Many of the US Army's Bell AH-1Gs, seen here, have been rebuilt to AH-1S standard.

Lower Right A trio of US Army Bell AH-1 gunships operating over Vietnam. In all, around 2,000 AH-1s of all models have been built by Bell.

helicopter, strap on the additional military hardware and be instantly equipped to go into the tank-killing business.

The drawback to this alternative is simply that it buys a limited operational capability, along with an aircraft with a very low tolerance even to light enemy ground fire. Such considerations notwithstanding, there are today numerous armies operating just such light armed helicopters that, so long as they maintain an element of surprise, could still inflict a considerable mauling on an advancing enemy armored ground force. Perhaps significantly, a number of European helicopter manufacturers are currently developing anti-armor gunships of their own in the shape of Italy's Agusta A129 Mangusta and the joint Franco-German PAH-2, both of which are aimed at costing less than the top-of-the-market AH-64.

Above A Westland Lynx AH1 of the British Army unleashing a salvo of anti-armor rocket projectiles.

Far Left This British Army Westland Lynx AH1 is capable of carrying up to eight TOW anti-tank missiles. Around 120 military Lynx have been sold to date.

Center The formidable Soviet Mil-24 'Hind' gunship has played a major role in countering Muslim partisans in Afghanistan.

Below Two US Marine Corps' Bell AH-1T Sea Cobras.

Far Left, Above and Left The US Army's latest tank-killer, the Hughes AH-64A Apache can operate in all weathers and carries up to 16 long range Hellfire anti-tank missiles as well as over 1,200 rounds of 30mm ammunition for its rapid-fire, electronically directed cannon.

Left and Lower Left Two revealing aspects of the Federal German Army's MBB Bo-105/PAH-1 tank-killer, equipped to carry six HOT anti-tank missiles.

Below and Bottom The Agusta A109, which, like the MBB Bo-105, started life as a commercial helicopter, has been bought by the armies of Argentina, Libya and Yugoslavia for anti-armor missions. More lately, Agusta have developed the more heavily armed and armored A129 Mangusta, on order for the Italian Army.

Left and Lower Left A TOIV anti-tank missile-equipped Hughes Model 500MD Defender.

Right and Below Two informative views of Sikorsky's militarized AUH-76 version of their S-76 MkII commercial machine. Ordered by the Philippines, the anti-armor AUH-76 can carry up to 16 TOW missiles, or 12 troops when operating as a utility transport.

CHAPTER 5
Into the Future

While the military and naval helicopter has provided a previously undreamt freedom to deploy and support ground or naval forces in a way not possible even with the latest and costly jump jets, they do have drawbacks. All helicopters suffer from two in-built limitations; a lack of speed relative to the fixed-winged aircraft, along with higher operating and maintenance costs compared with a fixed-winged machine capable of lifting the same load.

By the nature of the helicopter's complex and crucial rotating lift and control producing rotor systems, more parts require more frequent inspection and, in some cases, also need more frequent replacement than on a comparable fixed-wing aircraft. As these aspects are part and parcel of the helicopter's fundamental makeup, it is understandable that rotary-winged users have, on the whole, learnt to live with them. This is not to say that the complexity of helicopter rotor and power transmission systems have not been simplified somewhat over the years, but progress on these fronts is slow.

Limited top speed
The other major shortfall of the helicopter – that of its limited top speed – is also fundamental, for while it continues to rely on a rotating lift system, its rotor-tip speeds can readily be running into all of the problems associated with transonic flight even when the aircraft itself is flying at seemingly modest forward speed. Indeed, while a few specially designed or modified military helicopters have exceeded speeds of 200 mph, the vast majority have top

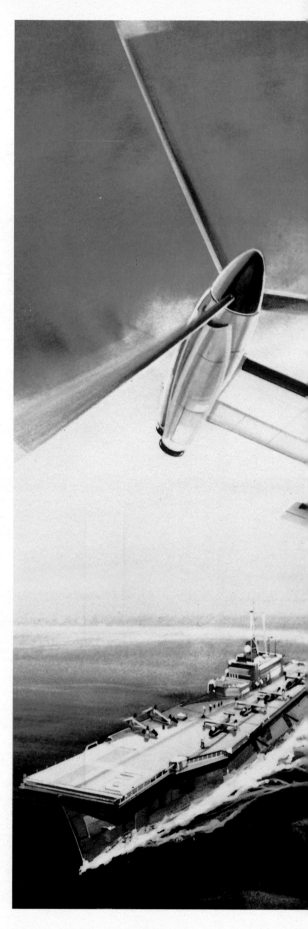

Right An artist's impression of the assault version of the Bell-Boeing JVX currently in full-scale development for the US Navy, Marines, Army and Air Force. Based on the successful Bell XV-15, the JVX employs tilting engine/rotors to take off vertically, yet fly like a conventional propeller-driven aircraft.

Above and Right Sikorsky
have amassed much flying
experience on their
Advancing Blade Concept
(ABC) XH-59A, dating back
to 1973.

speeds in the range between 125 mph to 160 mph. This said, there are a number of ways available with which to break through the helicopter's limited forward speed problem. One solution is to provide the machine with wings and some form of forward thrusting motive power, as in the case of the early 1930s autogyros.

More recently, helicopter designers have turned their attention, particularly in the US, to incorporating some form of main rotor system that will enable the machine to rise vertically under the thrust of rotation, after which the specially shaped rotor is stopped in such a position as to provide the same lift characteristics as that of a normal aircraft wing, as in the US-developed X-wing concept. Another approach to the problem currently being studied in the US is that of tilting the machine's engines and rotors as with the joint Boeing-Bell JVX design. With all of this effort going on, there is a distinct possibility that the 300 mph-plus half-helicopter-half-airplane is just around the corner.

Above A proposed Hughes Helicopters design for a light fast scouting helicopter.

Below Sikorsky have built this prototype helicopter specifically to gain in-flight experience with new lightweight material and construction techniques.

Upper Right and Lower Right The Sikorsky S-72 experimental airplane-cum-helicopter has been flown with and without wings and recently without rotors.

Picture acknowledgements

Aerospatiale – Division Helecoptere 18,
19, 44 top, 46-47 **Bell Helicopters** 15
bottom, 36, 48-49, 49 top **Boeing Vertol
Company** 14 bottom, 15 top **K.J.A.
Brookes** 4-5, 13 top, 24, 45 bottom **Hugh
Cowin** end papers, 7 top & bottom, 12, 16,
17, 20, 21 top, 22 bottom, 23 top, 28, 32, 33,
35 top, 39 top, 40, 41, 42-43, 44, 58-59, 63
bottom, Agusta 29, 38 top, Aviation
Photographs 7 center, Bell Helicopter
Company title page, 48 bottom, Boeing Vertol
Company 14 top, Hughes Helicopters Inc. 22
top, Sikorsky Aircraft 27, 63, US Navy 37 top,
VFW Fokker 6, Westland Helicopters Ltd. 51
top **Stuart Howe/USAF Museum** 9, 10
Hughes Helicopters Inc. 52, 53 top, 56, 62
top **Image in Industry Ltd.** 2, 50
MacClancey Collection front cover **MARS**
37 bottom, 39 bottom, 49 bottom, 53 bottom,
Agusta 55, Bell Helicopter Company 51
bottom, Boeing Vertol Company 8, 11, Crown
Copyright 3, MBB, Munich 23 bottom, 54 top,
Sikorsky Aircraft 6-7, 26-27, Westland
Helicopters Ltd. 24-25 **Messerschmitt-
Bülkow-Blohm** 54 bottom **Klaus Niska** 38
bottom, 51 center **Sikorsky Aircraft** 34, 35,
57, 60-61, 62 **US Department of Defense**
21 bottom **Westland Helicopters Ltd.**
30-31

Multimedia Publications (UK) Limited have
endeavored to observe the legal
requirements with regard to the rights of
suppliers of photographic material.